Revision Questions for Standard Grade

Physics

Campbell White

Formerly Principal Teacher of Physics
Tynecastle High School, Edinburgh
now Scottish Qualifications Authority

Editorial help by
Michael Batty
St Kentigern's Academy, Bathgate

Jim Lowrie
Edinburgh's Telford College

Published by
Chemcord
16 Inch Keith
East Kilbride
Glasgow

ISBN 1 870570 57 X

© White , 1995
reprinted 2004

Printed by Bell & Bain, Glasgow

CONTENTS

INTRODUCTION

This book has been written in the firm belief that to become good at Physics you need to do more than read revision notes a couple of times. If you really want to <u>understand</u> Physics then you must take an active role and work on questions.

The questions in this book cover all of the Learning Outcomes of Standard Grade Physics. They are arranged by Unit and Section of the Physics syllabus.

Since the questions are based on the Learning Outcomes, most cover Knowledge and Understanding. There are also a significant number of questions that fall into the Problem Solving category. The questions in the book have not, however, been categorised as either K & U or PS.

If you can answer all of the questions honestly and correctly you will at least have a very good grasp of the basics of Physics and hopefully are on the way to a pass in Physics, However, the only way you will be able to answer questions on Physics (or any other subject for that matter) is if you have made the effort to learn the subject. There is no substitute for good old-fashioned learning - of formulae and how to use them and of facts and what they relate to.

The answers to numerical questions are given at the end of the book. A separate answer book is available which contains full answers to all the questions in this book. The question and answer books together form an aid which enables you to <u>actively</u> revise the whole of your Physics course.

Questions (or parts of questions) in *italics* relate to Credit Level. All others relate to General Level.

Notes

- Throughout this book, 'm/s' has been used for the unit of speed. You should also be aware of the alternative ways of writing this unit, since you may meet them in your work. The other ways are 'metres per second' and 'm s^{-1}'. The same applies to the unit of acceleration and all other derived units.

HINTS ON ANSWERING QUESTIONS

- It is easy to cut corners with numerical questions - but it is also easy to lose marks if you do cut corners. In the final exam if you do not show your working and your answer is wrong, you will be given no marks. However, if you have only made an arithmetical mistake and shown all of your working, you might only lose half a mark. Follow the stages set out in the example below for all numerical problems.

  A pupil uses two sound operated switches, 1.7 m apart, connected to an interface and a computer, to obtain a value for the speed of sound. The computer records a time of 5 ms.
  Calculate the value that these results give for the speed of sound.

For numerical questions, read the question and write down the information given in a column as quantity, value and unit. If the unit given is not the S.I. unit (System International - the basic units), then convert to S.I.

distance $= 1.7$ m
time $= 5$ ms $= 5 \times 10^{-3}$ s $= 0.005$ s

Decide which equation or equations to use by considering the information given and the quantity to be found.

$$\text{speed} = \frac{\text{distance}}{\text{time}} \qquad v = \frac{d}{t}$$

Substitute the given numbers for the quantities in the equation and rearrange it if necessary. Do the calculation and write down the answer with the correct units.

$$v = \frac{d}{t} = \frac{1.7}{0.005} = \underline{340 \text{ m/s}}$$

- Learn the correct units for all quantities and write them in the final answer to questions - a wrong or missing unit will lose half a mark.

- Know how to use your calculator correctly, especially for numbers of the form 5×10^{-3} (Scientific Notation). This is usually keyed into a calculator as:

(The $\boxed{\text{EXP}}$ button means "times ten to the power of ----")

- Know how to interpret an answer on your calculator correctly. An answer of 5×10^{-3} may be displayed on a calculator as 5 -3; 05 -03; 5 -03; 5^{-3} or 5 E -3. If you write any of these versions as a final answer, you will lose half a mark.

- Be sensible about how you quote an answer given on a calculator. For example, the calculator answer to 56 divided by 23 is 2.4347826. Since the original numbers were only quoted to two significant figures, to quote the answer given by the calculator is wrong because it suggests that the answer is known to eight significant figures. Quote this answer as 2.4 or 2.43. Watch out for questions that give numbers like this.

- With non-numerical questions, for example, a description of an experiment, answer the question that is asked, not the one that you hoped would be asked. So if the question asks for a description of an experiment to calculate the instantaneous speed of a trolley, do not write about two light gates separated by several metres - this would give an average speed.

- It might be obvious but it is worth repeating - if you leave a multiple choice question blank you will gain no marks. With a guess you have a one in five chance of being correct. But the best solution of all is to know the work well enough to be able to answer without guessing.

- If you are asked in a question to give two reasons or examples and you are not sure what to answer so you give three, one of which is wrong, the mark gained for one of the correct ones will be lost because of the wrong answer. This is to avoid the 'stab in the dark' answers. To save this happening, again you must know your work and only answer the question that is asked.

- Use the size of space left for an exam question as a guide to how much to write but do not be put off if you have answered a question in less space. Do not be tempted to write just to fill up the space.

- Read what you are being told to do in a question. 'Calculate' tells you to use an equation to work out an answer. 'State' simply asks you to write down what you understand about a part of Physics whereas for an 'explain' question you should write down why some part of Physics is as it is.

- If you are told to refer to the Data Sheet or you need to use a value which is not given in a question (the speed of sound in air for example) then use the information given. A mark will probably be allocated for using this information in the question.

DATA SHEET

Speed of light in materials

Material	Speed in m/s
Air	3.0×10^8
Carbon dioxide	3.0×10^8
Diamond	1.2×10^8
Glass	2.0×10^8
Glycerol	2.1×10^8
Water	2.3×10^8

Melting and boiling points of materials

Material	Melting point in ^oC	Boiling point in ^oC
Alcohol	–98	65
Aluminium	660	2470
Copper	1077	2567
Glycerol	18	290
Lead	328	1737
Turpentine	–10	156

Speed of sound in materials

Material	Speed in m/s
Aluminium	5200
Air	340
Bone	3000
Carbon dioxide	270
Glycerol	1900
Muscle	1600
Steel	5200
Tissue	1500
Water	1500

Specific heat capacity of materials

Material	Specific heat capacity in J/kg/^oC
Alcohol	2350
Aluminium	902
Copper	386
Glass	500
Glycerol	2400
Ice	2100
Lead	128
Silica	1033
Water	4180

Gravitational field strengths

Heavenly body	Gravitational field strength on the surface in N/kg
Earth	10
Jupiter	26
Mars	4
Mercury	4
Moon	1.6
Neptune	12
Saturn	11
Sun	270
Venus	9

Specific latent heat of fusion of materials

Material	Specific latent heat of fusion in J/kg
Alcohol	0.99×10^5
Aluminium	3.95×10^5
Carbon Dioxide	1.80×10^5
Copper	2.05×10^5
Glycerol	1.81×10^5
Water	3.34×10^5

Specific latent heat of vaporisation of materials

Material	Specific latent heat of vaporisation in J/kg
Alcohol	11.20×10^5
Carbon Dioxide	3.77×10^5
Glycerol	8.30×10^5
Water	22.60×10^5

Unit 1 - Telecommunication

Section 1 - Communication Using Waves

1. What is meant by **telecommunication**?

2. What is the approximate speed of sound in air?

3. At what speed does light travel?

4. Give <u>one</u> example which illustrates the difference between the speed of light and the speed of sound in air.

5. Describe a method of measuring the speed of sound in air.
   A labelled diagram may help your description.

6. Explain why it is necessary to use a timing device which can accurately measure a very short time period (such as a microcomputer) <u>or</u> to use a very long distance when measuring the speed of sound.

7. (a) State the relationship between distance, time and speed, using the symbols that are used for these quantities.

   (b) What is the unit, and its abbreviation, that is used to measure each quantity?

8. If the speed of sound is 340 m/s, calculate how far a sound will travel in 5 s.

9. A pupil uses two sound operated switches, 1.7 m apart, connected to an interface and a computer, to obtain a value for the speed of sound. The computer records a time of 5 ms.
   What value do these results give for the speed of sound?
   (Remember 'ms' is the abbreviation for milliseconds.)

10. Explain why it is <u>not</u> necessary to use the speed of light in problems involving both a flash of light and a burst of sound.

11. During a thunderstorm, a girl notices that the sound of thunder comes 3 s after she has seen the flash of lightning.
    If the speed of sound in air is 340 m/s, calculate the distance from the girl to the storm.

12. A lighthouse sends out a flash of light and a burst of sound at the same time.
    If the speed of sound in air is 340 m/s, how long after the light is seen will an observer on the bridge of a ship 1.36 km away hear the sound?

13. Copy and complete:

    Because waves transmit _____ from one place to another, they can be used to send _____ .

14. What is a **wave**?
    (This question is more difficult to answer than it appears!)

15. (a) What is meant by the **frequency** of a wave?

    (b) What is the symbol that is used for frequency?

    (c) What is the unit, and its abbreviation, that is used to measure frequency?

16. (a) What is meant by the **wavelength** of a wave?

    (b) What is the symbol that is used for wavelength?

    (c) What is the unit, and its abbreviation, that is used to measure wavelength?

17. (a) What is meant by the **speed** or **velocity** of a wave?

    (b) What is the symbol that is used for wave speed?

    (c) What is the unit, and its abbreviation, that is used to measure wave speed?

18. (a) What is meant by the **amplitude** of a wave?

    (b) What is the symbol that is used for amplitude?

    (c) What is the unit, and its abbreviation, that is used to measure amplitude?

19. (a) Draw a diagram of a wave.

    (b) Mark the following on your diagram:
    a crest;
    a trough;
    one wavelength;
    the amplitude.

20. Water waves move a distance of 10 m in 4 s.
    Calculate the wave speed.

21. Calculate how far water waves travel in 5 s if the wave speed is 3 m/s.

22. Calculate how long it takes water waves to travel a distance of 15 m if the wave speed is 5 m/s.

23. State the relationship between speed, frequency and wavelength, using the symbols that are used for these quantities.

24. A wave generator in a swimming pool has a frequency of 10 Hz. The wavelength of the waves it produces is measured at 40 cm.
    Calculate the speed of the waves.

25. A tuning fork produces a note of 262 Hz.
    Calculate the wavelength of the waves produced in air when the wave speed is 340 m/s.

26. Calculate how many times a boat will bob up and down in a second if it is in a harbour with waves of wavelength 50 cm travelling at 25 cm/s.

27. *What is the relationship between wave period T and wave frequency f?*

28. *Explain how wave frequency multiplied by wavelength is equal to distance divided by time for a wave.*

Section 2 - Communication Using Cables

1. Describe a method of sending a message using code.

2. (a) What is the purpose of the **transmitter** in a communications system?

    (b) What is the purpose of the **receiver** in a communications system?

3. Give an example of long range communication using wires between the transmitter and the receiver.

4. (a) What energy change takes place in a **microphone**?

    (b) What energy change takes place in a **loudspeaker**?

5. (a) What type of device is contained in the **mouthpiece** of a telephone (the transmitter)?

    (b) What type of device is contained in the **earpiece** of a telephone (the receiver)?

6. What is transmitted along the communicating wires during a telephone conversation?

7. At what speed is a telephone signal transmitted?

8. What is the name of the instrument that can be used to look at the patterns of electrical waves in wires?

9. Describe what is meant by the **frequency** of a sound.

10. Describe what is meant by the **amplitude** of a sound.

11. Copy and complete the following diagrams to show the signal patterns obtained when the sound signals are as stated.

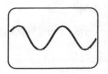

Quiet sound, low frequency   **Quiet sound, high frequency**

Loud sound, low frequency   **Loud sound, high frequency**

12. *Explain how the electrical signal pattern in telephone wires is related to the loudness and frequency of the sound signal producing it.*

13. What is an **optical fibre**?

14. Describe <u>one</u> practical example of telecommunication which uses optical fibres.

15. *Both electrical cables and optical fibres are used in some telecommunication systems.*
    Optical fibres have many advantages over electrical cables.
    Give at least <u>seven</u> of these advantages.

16. How do rays of light travel?

17. What happens to a ray of light when it meets a mirror?

18. (a) Draw a labelled diagram showing a ray of light being reflected from a plane (flat) mirror.

    (b) Describe the direction of the reflected ray of light from a flat mirror, in relation to the direction of the incident ray.

19. *The paths of rays of light show the **principle of reversibility**.*
    What does this principle state?

20. By what means are signals transmitted along an optical fibre?

21. *What is meant by **refraction of light**?*

22. *(a) Explain what is meant by the **critical angle**.*

    (b) Draw a labelled diagram to show the critical angle for a ray of light in a glass block.

23. *Explain what is meant by **total internal reflection**.*
    A labelled diagram will help your explanation.

24. *(a)   Copy and complete the diagram below to show how a ray of light travels from one end of an optical fibre to the other.*

    (b) Mark the angles of incidence and reflection on your diagram.

25. What is the approximate speed of signals which are transmitted along a glass opitical fibre?

26. If a glass optical fibre communication link was to be laid between Buenos Aires and London it would be 11 000 km long.
    Calculate how long it would take for a message to be transmitted along this link.

Section 3 - Radio and Television

1. Name the <u>six</u> main parts of a radio receiver on the block diagram below.

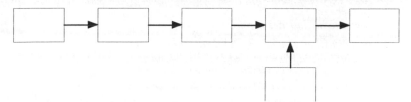

2. Describe the job that is done by each of the six main parts of a radio receiver.

3. *Describe, in general terms, how radio waves are transmitted and received.*
   Include in your description:
      what the **radio transmitter** *does;*
      what a **carrier wave** *is and why it is necessary to use a carrier wave for radio transmission;*
      what is meant by the term **amplitude modulation, a.m.** *(include a diagram);*
      what the **radio receiver** *does.*

4. Name the main parts of a television receiver (other than the electricity supply) on the block diagram below.

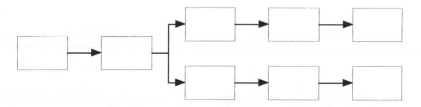

5. Describe the job that is done by each of the main parts of a television receiver, including the electricity supply.

6. *Describe, in general terms, how television waves are transmitted and received.*
   Include in your description:
      what the **television transmitter** *does;*
      what a **television carrier wave** *is and what its purpose is;*
      what is meant by the term **modulation***;*
      what the **receiver** *does.*

7. Describe how a picture is produced on a television screen.

8. *Explain what a television picture tube is and how it operates.*

9. *Describe how a moving picture is seen on a black and white television screen.*
   Include in your description:
       how the picture is built up of **lines***;*
       what is meant by **image retention (persistence of vision)** *and the part it plays in viewing a moving picture:*
       how the **brightness** *of the picture is changed.*

10. What are the <u>three</u> **primary colours** for mixing lights?

11. How are all the colours seen on a colour television screen produced?

12. *What are the <u>three</u> secondary colours for mixing lights?*

13. *Copy and complete the table showing which colour of light is produced when each of the coloured lights mentioned are mixed.*

Red	+	**Green**	*only*	*produces*	_____
Red	+	**Blue**	*only*	*produces*	_____
Green	+	**Blue**	*only*	*produces*	_____
Red	+	**Green**	+ **Blue**	*produces*	_____

Section 4 - Transmission of Radio Waves

1. Radio and television are examples of long range communication.

   (a) List some of the <u>advantages</u> of radio communication over other means of communication.

   (b) List some of the <u>disadvantages</u> of radio communication over other means of communication.

   (c) Give one other example of long range communication that does not need cables.

2. In what form do microwaves, radio and television signals travel through space?

3. What do microwaves, radio and television signals transfer from place to place?

4. What is the speed of microwaves, radio and television signals through air and space?

5. *Calculate how far away the Moon is if it takes 1.2 s for a radio signal sent from a beacon on the Moon to be received on Earth.*

6. What quantities can be used to identify a particular radio transmitter?

7. *BBC Radio 5 Live broadcasts on a frequency of 909 kHz.*
   Calculate the wavelength of the radio waves transmitted.

8. *The wavelength of the radio waves transmitted by the Max AM radio transmitter is 194 m.*
   Calculate the frequency allocated to the Max AM radio station.

9. *Explain what is meant by **diffraction** of a wave.*

10. *Show, by using diagrams, which is diffracted more, a long wavelength wave or a short wavelength wave.*

11. *Explain in terms of diffraction how wavelength affects radio and television reception.*

12. *Explain why long waves in the low frequency radio band travel long distances.*

13. *Why are high frequency waves in the medium waveband used for local radio?*

14. *Why can high frequency waves in the short waveband be used for worldwide communication?*

15. *What property of waves in the VHF (very high frequency) waveband makes them <u>unsuitable</u> for long range communication?*

16. *What property of microwaves makes them <u>suitable</u> for satellite communication?*

17. (a) What is the purpose of curved reflectors on aerials or receivers?

    (b) Explain how curved reflectors on aerials or receivers do their job. A labelled diagram will help your explanation.

18. *Use a labelled diagram to explain why curved reflectors are used with some transmitters.*

19. Describe an application of curved reflectors used in telecommunication. In your description you should mention:
    satellites;
    microwave links;
    repeater stations;
    boosters.

20. What is meant by the **period** of a satellite?

21. What does the period of a satellite depend upon?

22. Explain what is meant by a **geostationary** satellite.

23. Why is world-wide communication difficult <u>without</u> the use of satellites?

24. Describe how telecommunication from one continent to another is possible using geostationary satellites and ground stations.

UNIT 2 - USING ELECTRICITY

Section 1 - From the Wall Socket

1. What is the purpose of the **mains supply** or **battery** in an electrical circuit?

2. What is the job done by all electrical appliances?

3. Describe the main energy change or changes in each of the following household appliances:
   toaster; table lamp; hair dryer; CD player; kettle; light bulb; vacuum cleaner; electric fire.

4. Explain what is meant by the **power rating** of a household appliance.

5. As a very general rule, which types of household appliances have the highest power ratings?

6. Give the approximate power ratings of each of the following household appliances:
   toaster; hair dryer; kettle; light bulb; electric fire; shaver; cooker.

7. What is the purpose of the **flexible cable** (flex) attached to a household appliance?

8. (a) What factor is used to decide the size of flex attached to a household appliance?

   (b) Explain what can happen if too thin a flex is connected to a household appliance.

9. (a) What is the purpose of the **fuse** in a plug?

   (b) Explain how a fuse does the job that it is designed to do.

10. (a) State the two sizes of fuse recommended for use in plugs.

    (b) Explain how to choose the correct fuse to use in the plug of a household appliance.

11. The table below gives information about some flexes that are available.

Flex type	Area of conductor (mm²)	Flex current rating (A)	For appliances of power rating up to
A	0.50	3	720 W
B	0.75	6	1440 W
C	1.00	10	2440 W
D	1.25	13	3120 W
E	1.50	16	3840 W

Copy and complete the following table for each of the household appliances mentioned to show:

(a) which flex is the most suitable;

(b) which size of fuse to use in the plug.

Appliance	Power (W)	Flex type	Fuse size
Deep fat fryer	3000		
Bedside lamp	100		
Sandwich maker	1000		
Television	300		

12. Explain why some household appliances, such as vacuum cleaners, which have electric motors, may need a 13 A fuse even although their constant power rating is less than 700 W.

13. State the colour of the insulation used for each of the following wires in the flex of a household appliance:

(a)   live;

(b)   neutral;

(c)   earth.

14. To which pin in a mains plug are each of the three wires of a flex connected?

15. The human body is a poor conductor of electricity.
    What makes it into a better conductor?

16. What is the purpose of the **earth wire** in an electrical installation?

17. *Explain the difference between the **live** and **neutral** terminals of the wall socket.*

18. *Explain how the earth wire does the job that it is designed to do.*

19. *Explain why fuses and switches must be in the live wire.*

20. (a) State why electrical appliances which have the **double insulation symbol** only need a 2 core flex while other appliances need a 3 core flex.

    (b) Draw the double insulation symbol.

21. State what the danger is in the following situations involving electricity and explain how they could result in accidents:

    (a) using electricity near water;

    (b) using the wrong size of fuse in a plug;

    (c) using the wrong type of flex;

    (d) using frayed or badly connected flex;

    (e) allowing a short circuit;

    (f) plugging too many appliances into one socket using a multiway adaptor.

Section 2 - Alternating and Direct Current

1. Explain what is meant by **alternating current** (a.c.).

2. Explain what is meant by **direct current** (d.c.).

3. State which of the two types of electricity, a.c. or d.c., is supplied by:

   (a) the mains supply;

   (b) a battery.

4. Draw the pattern which would be seen on a suitably adjusted oscilloscope when it is connected to:

   (a)   a source obtained from the mains supply;

   (b)   a battery.

5. What is the **frequency** of the mains supply in Britain?

6. What is the **mains voltage** quoted as in Britain?

7. *(a) Which is greater, the **quoted value** of an alternating voltage or the peak value of the same voltage?*

   (b) Explain why there is a difference between the quoted value of an alternating voltage and the peak value of the same voltage.

8. Draw the circuit symbol for each of the following components: a cell; a battery; a fuse; a lamp; a switch; a resistor; a capacitor; a diode; a variable resistor.

9. Starting at the source of energy and working clockwise, name the components in each of the following circuits:

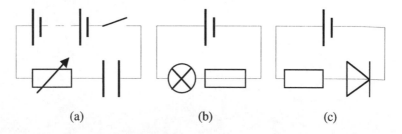

   (a)   (b)   (c)

10. What is the difference between an **electrical conductor** and an **insulator**?

11. Which kind of charge is carried on an electron?

12. What is an **electric current**?

13. (a) What is the symbol that is used for electric current?

    (b) What is the unit, and its abbreviation, that is used to measure electric current?

14. *(a) What is the symbol that is used for **electric charge**?*

    (b) What is the unit, and its abbreviation, that is used to measure electric charge?

15. *State the relationship between charge, current and time.*

16. *Calculate the current in a circuit when a charge of 180 C is transferred in 1 minute.*

17. *Calculate the charge transferred in a circuit which has a current of 0.25 A for 1 hour.*

18. *What is meant by the **voltage** of a supply?*

19. (a) What is the symbol that is used for voltage?

    (b) What is the unit, and its abbreviation, that is used to measure voltage?

20. Two quantities in electricity that are not the same but are often confused are **voltage** and **current**.
    Show that you understand these quantities by explaining what is meant by each of them.

Section 3 - Resistance

1. (a) What type of meter is used to measure **current**?

   (b) What type of meter is used to measure **voltage**?

2. (a) Draw the circuit symbol for an **ammeter**.

   (b) Draw the circuit symbol for a **voltmeter**.

3. (a) Describe how an ammeter is connected into a circuit.

   (b) Describe how a voltmeter is connected into a circuit.

4. Redraw the following circuit to include a meter to measure the current in the resistor and a meter to measure the voltage across the lamp.

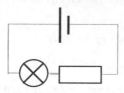

5. Explain what is meant by the **resistance** of a wire.

6. (a) What is the symbol that is used for resistance?

   (b) What is the unit, and its abbreviation, that is used to measure resistance?

7. State what happens to the current in a circuit when the resistance in it is <u>increased</u>.

8. State the relationship between resistance, current and voltage for a resistor.

9. State **Ohm's Law** for a conductor.

10. What is the ratio V/I for a resistor called?

11. What happens to the ratio V/I for a resistor when the current in the resistor changes?

12. A car headlamp bulb takes a current of 3 A from the 12 V car battery. Calculate its resistance.

13. Calculate the current taken from a 9 V battery by a resistor of resistance 180 Ω.

14. Calculate the voltage across a 1 kΩ resistor when the current in it is 10 mA.

15. What is the purpose of a **variable resistor** in a circuit?

16. Give <u>two</u> practical uses for variable resistors.

17. Name <u>two</u> electrical components which have a resistance that changes due to a change in the physical conditions.

18. State what happens to the electrical energy when there is a current in a wire.

19. Name <u>three</u> appliances used in the home in which electrical energy is changed into heat.

20. In which part of an electric heater does the energy change take place?

21. What are the <u>two</u> forms of energy that electrical energy is changed into in a lamp?

22. There are two types of electric lamps commonly used, **filament lamps** and **discharge tubes**.
    State where the energy change takes place in:

    (a) a filament lamp;

    (b) a discharge tube.

23. (a) Which type of lamp is more efficient, a filament lamp or a discharge tube?

    (b) Why is one type of lamp more efficient than the other?

24. Explain how electrical energy is used up in an electrical circuit.

25. (a) What is the symbol that is used for **energy**?

    (b) What is the unit, and its abbreviation, that is used to measure energy?

26. Explain what is meant by **power**.

27. State the relationship between power, energy and time.

28. (a) What is the symbol that is used for power?

(b) What is the unit, and its abbreviation, that is used to measure power?

(c) How is the unit of power related to the joule?

29. Calculate the amount of energy transferred in a 150 W light bulb every minute.

30. State the relationship between the rate at which electrical energy is transformed, voltage and current.

31. A car headlamp bulb takes a current of 3 A from the 12 V car battery. Calculate its power rating.

32. Calculate the current taken from the mains by a 230 W television.

33. *Show how V I and I ^{2} R are both equal to each other and are both expressions used to find electrical power.*

34. *Calculate the amount of electrical energy transformed into other forms of energy every second in a 10 kΩ resistor when the current in it is 5 mA.*

35. *A 60 W light bulb takes a current of 0.25 A.*
    Calculate its resistance.

36. *Explain why the heating element of an electric fire gets hot while the flex which connects the fire to the mains does not.*

Section 4 - Useful Circuits

1. Describe what is meant by a **series circuit**.
   Use a diagram to help your description.

2. Make a statement about the current at all points in a series circuit.

3. What is the relationship between the voltage of the supply and the other voltages in a series circuit?

4. In the circuit shown, all of the resistors are identical.
   Copy the diagram and fill in the values on all of the meters (including units).

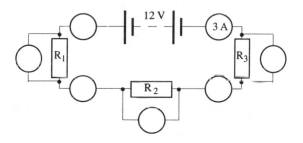

5. State an application in the home that uses <u>two</u> switches in series.

6. Describe what is meant by a **parallel circuit**.
   Use a diagram to help your description.

7. Make a statement about the current drawn from the supply in a parallel circuit.

8. Make a statement about the voltage across components in a parallel circuit.

9. In the circuit shown all of the bulbs are identical.
   Copy the diagram and fill in the values on all of the meters (including units).

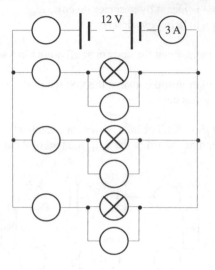

10. Explain why connecting too many appliances to one socket is dangerous.

11. *Draw a circuit diagram to show how all four car sidelights are connected to the car battery when switched on.*

12. *Draw a circuit diagram to show how the two headlamps in a car can only be switched on when the ignition switch and the light switch are both on.*

13. *Car brake lights only go on when the ignition is switched on and the brake switch is pressed.*
    Draw the circuit diagram for this arrangement.

14. *The interior light in a car goes on when either the driver's door or the passenger's door is opened.*

    (a) What happens to the door switch when a door is opened?

    (b) Draw the circuit diagram used to switch the light on.

15. Explain what is meant by an **open circuit**.

16. Explain what is meant by a **short circuit**.

17. Describe how to make a simple **continuity tester** using a battery and a bulb.
    Include a diagram of the circuit used in your description.

18. Describe how a continuity tester can be used to test for faults in a circuit.

19. What is the reading on an ohmmeter when it is placed across an **open circuit**?

20. What is the reading on an ohmmeter when it is placed across a **short circuit**?

21. (a) Draw a diagram showing <u>three</u> resistors R_1, R_2 and R_3 in series.

    (b) State the relationship between these resistors and R_T, the total resistance.

22. (a) Draw a diagram showing <u>three</u> resistors R_1, R_2 and R_3 in parallel.

    (b) State the relationship between these resistors and R_T, the total resistance.

23. Calculate the total resistance in the following circuit.

$$\boxed{R_1} \quad \boxed{R_2} \quad \boxed{R_3}$$
56 Ω   22 Ω   47 Ω

24. Calculate the total resistance in the following circuit.

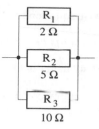

R_1
2 Ω

R_2
5 Ω

R_3
10 Ω

Section 5 - Behind the Wall

1. Are appliances connected in series or in parallel when they are connected to the mains through the wiring of a house?

2. Is the **lighting circuit** in a house a series circuit or a parallel circuit?

3. *Describe what is meant by a **ring main circuit**.*
   Use a circuit diagram to help your description.

4. *What are the advantages of using a ring main circuit instead of a simple parallel circuit?*

5. *Give two differences between the lighting circuit and the ring main circuit in the wiring of a house.*

6. (a) What is the purpose of the **mains fuses** in the mains wiring of a house?

   (b) Explain how the mains fuses do the job that they are designed to do.

7. (a) Explain why more than one mains fuse is necessary in the mains wiring of a house.

   (b) Explain why different values of mains fuses are required in the mains wiring of a house.

8. (a) What is a **circuit breaker**?

   (b) What can a circuit breaker be used to replace?

9. *Give one reason why a circuit breaker is better than a fuse.*

10. What is the purpose of the electricity meter in the wiring of a house?

11. What is the unit that the electricity supply companies use to measure the amount of electrical energy consumed?

12. *Explain, by doing a calculation, how the two units the **kilowatt-hour** and the **joule** are related.*

Section 6 - Movement from Electricity

1. (a) What is a **magnetic field**?

   (b) How can a magnetic field be represented?

2. What effect does an electric current in a wire produce in the space around the wire?

3. Draw the magnetic field around a straight current-carrying wire.

4. Draw the magnetic field around a coil of wire carrying a current.

5. What is an **electromagnet**?

6. Give <u>two</u> examples of practical applications of electromagnets.

7. *A wire carrying a current experiences a force when it is placed in a magnetic field.*
   What <u>two</u> variables does the direction of this force depend upon?

8. Name the parts labelled **A**, **B**, **C** and **D** on the diagram of an electric motor.

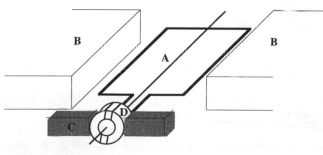

9. *Explain how an electric motor operates*
   Your explanation should include:
   the forces that act on the coil;
   the purpose of the brushes;
   the purpose of the commutator.

10. *Why do commercial motors use* **carbon brushes**?

11. *Why do commercial motors use* **multi-section commutators**?

12. *Why do commercial motors use* **field coils**?

UNIT 3 - HEALTH PHYSICS

Section 1 - The Use of Thermometers

1. (a) What is a **thermometer**?

   (b) What do all thermometers have in common?

2. What is meant by the **temperature** of an object?

3. What is the name of the scale used to measure temperature?

4. (a) Name <u>four</u> different types of thermometer.

   (b) For each type, give the physical property that changes with temperature.

5. Describe how a liquid in glass thermometer operates.
   Include a labelled diagram in your description.

6. (a) List the main differences between a clinical thermometer and an ordinary thermometer.

   (b) Give a reason for each of the differences you have mentioned.

7. Describe how to measure someone's body temperature using a clinical thermometer.

8. What is the approximate body temperature of a healthy person?

9. Explain how knowing a patient's body temperature can help a doctor decide what is wrong with the patient.

10. What is meant by **hypothermia**?

Section 2 - Using Sound

1. (a) Explain what causes sounds.

   (b) Explain how sounds are transmitted from one place to another.

2. Why can sounds <u>not</u> travel through a vacuum?

3. Describe how a stethoscope works.
   Use a labelled diagram to help your description.

4. What is the approximate range of human hearing?

5. What is meant by **ultrasound**?

6. Give an example of the use of ultrasound in medicine.

7. *(a) Describe how ultrasound can be used to take 'pictures' of the inside of the body.*

   (b) Draw a simple diagram showing the positions of the transmitter, the body and the receiver when an ultrasound scan is given.

   (c) What property of waves is employed when ultrasound is used to examine a body?

8. What is **sonar** equipment used for?

9. What is the unit that is used to measure **noise level**?

10. What is meant by **noise pollution**?

11. Give <u>two</u> examples of noise pollution.

12. (a) What is the noise level of the least sound that can be heard (the threshold of hearing)?

    (b) What is the approximate noise level of normal conversation in an average room?

13. How do ear protectors prevent permanent damage to hearing due to excessive noise?

Section 3 - Light and Sight

1. What is meant by **refraction of light**?

2. Draw a labelled diagram to show the path of a ray of light which passes from air into glass.

3. *(a) Draw a labelled diagram showing a ray of light being refracted. Include in your diagram:*
      the incident ray;
      the refracted ray;
      the normal.

   (b) Label the angle of incidence and the angle of refraction on your diagram.

4. Draw a **convex (converging) lens** and show what it does to parallel rays of light passing through it.

5. Draw a **concave (diverging) lens** and show what it does to parallel rays of light passing through it.

6. Draw a simple diagram of an **eye** and label the following parts:
      the iris and the pupil;
      the cornea and the lens;
      the retina and the optic nerve.

7. Describe how light is focused on the retina of the eye.

8. What differences are there between an object and the image of it that appears on the retina of the eye?

9. Draw a labelled ray diagram to show how an inverted image is formed on the retina of the eye.

10. *The eye is able to focus on objects which are some distance away as well as objects which are close to it. This is called **accommodation**. How is the eye able to do this?*

11. *Draw a ray diagram to show how the lens of the eye forms an image of an object which is some distance from the eye.*

12. *Draw a ray diagram to show how the lens of the eye forms an image of an object which is close to the eye.*

13. What is meant by **long sight**?

14. What is meant by **short sight**?

15. How can long and short sight be corrected?

16. *Draw a ray diagram to show how long sight can be corrected.*

17. *Draw a ray diagram to show how short sight can be corrected.*

18. What is meant by the **focal length** of a convex lens?

19. Describe a simple experiment to find the focal length of a convex lens.

20. *What is meant by the **power** of a lens?*

21. *What is the unit that is used to measure the power of a lens?*

22. *State the equation that links the power and the focal length of a lens.*

23. *Calculate the power of a convex lens of focal length 40 cm.*

24. *Calculate the focal length of a concave lens which has a power of 10 D.*

25. Fibre optics can be used to transmit **cold light**.
    What is meant by cold light?

26. *(a) What is an **endoscope (fibrescope)**?*

    (b) Explain how an endoscope works.
    A labelled diagram will help your answer.

Section 4 - Using the Spectrum

1. What is a **laser**?

2. Describe why a laser is sometimes called a 'bloodless scalpel'.

3. Give three uses for a laser in medicine.

4. One use of X-rays in medicine is to find broken bones.
   Explain how this is done.

5. What can be used to detect X-rays?

6. Draw a simple diagram showing the relative positions of the X-ray transmitter, the patient's body and the detector of the X-rays.

7. *Describe what is meant by* **computerised tomography**.

8. *What advantages does computerised tomography have over a simple X-ray?*

9. What is another name for infrared radiation?

10. What is a **thermogram**?

11. Give one example of how infrared radiation is used for treatment in medicine.

12. Give one example of how infrared radiation is used for diagnosis in medicine.

13. Give two examples of how ultraviolet radiation is used in medicine.

14. Give one danger of too much exposure to ultraviolet radiation.

15. Place these three radiations in order of increasing wavelength:
    infrared;
    ultraviolet;
    visible light.

Section 5 - Nuclear Radiation - Humans and Medicine

1. What effects can radiation have on living cells?

2. Give <u>two</u> medical uses of radiation based on the fact that radiation can destroy cells.

3. Give <u>one</u> medical use of radiation based on the fact that radiation is easy to detect.

4. Name the <u>three</u> types of radiation.

5. Which type of radiation is best at penetrating the human body?

6. Explain what is meant by a **tracer**, and describe how tracers can be used in medicine.

7. When radiation passes through a body, what can happen to the energy it carries?

8. State the range in air of all three types of radiation.

9. State the minimum amount of material that will absorb each of the three types of radiation.

10. Describe a simple model of an atom.
    Include a labelled diagram to help your description.

11. What are the relative masses of each of the particles that make up an atom?

12. (a) State the type of charge carried by each of the following particles:
    (i)   proton;
    (ii) electron;
    (iii) neutron.

    (b) Why is an atom normally uncharged when it consists of charged particles?

13. *When radiation passes through a material it can **ionise** the atoms of that material.*
    Explain what is meant by the ionisation of atoms.

14. Which of the three types of radiation produces the greatest amount of ionisation of atoms?

15. (a) Give <u>three</u> examples of the effects of radiation on non-living things.

    (b) For each of the three examples, describe how the effect is used in a detector of radiation, naming the detector in each case.

16. (a) What is the unit used to measure the **activity** of a radioactive source?

    (b) How is this unit defined?

17. What happens to the activity of a radioactive source as time goes on?

18. *What is meant by the **half-life** of a radioactive source?*

19. *Explain why it is necessary to define the activity of a radioactive source in terms of half-life.*

20. *What is meant by **background radiation**?*

21. *Describe a method of measuring the half-life of a radioactive element.*

22. *A radioactive source has a half-life of 15 days.
    What is its activity 60 days after it was measured at 1600 kBq?*

23. *In 6 years, the activity of a source drops from 200 kBq to 25 kBq.
    What is the half-life of the source?*

24. Describe <u>four</u> safety precautions which it is necessary to take when dealing with radioactive substances.

25. *State <u>three</u> factors that the biological effect of radiation depends upon.*

26. What is the unit that is used to measure **equivalent dose** ?

27. *What is the significance of equivalent dose ?*

UNIT 4 - ELECTRONICS

Section 1 - Overview

1. What are the three main parts that an electronic system can be split into?

2. Draw a **block diagram** showing how the three parts of an electronic system are linked.

3. The output of an electronic system can be either **digital** or **analogue**. Explain what is meant by each of these two types of output.

4. (a) Draw an analogue signal as it may be viewed on an oscilloscope.

   (b) Draw a digital signal as it may be viewed on an oscilloscope.

5. (a) Give one example of an analogue electronic signal.

   (b) Give one example of a digital electronic signal.

6. (a) Give one example of an instrument that has an analogue display.

   (b) Give one example of an instrument that has a digital display.

Section 2 - Output Devices

1. What is meant by an **output device** in an electronic system?

2. (a) Give <u>six</u> examples of output devices.

   (b) For each of your examples, give the output energy that the input electrical energy is changed into.

   (c) For each of the examples, indicate whether it is a digital output device or an analogue output device.

3. Explain how a lamp can be used as <u>either</u> a digital <u>or</u> an analogue output device.

4. What is a **solenoid**?

5. What is a **relay**?

6. *Give a suitable output device for each of the following situations:*

   (a) a system to turn a conveyor belt round in a bottling factory;

   (b) to push the chosen packet of sweets to the hatch in a confectionery machine;

   (c) as an audible warning when an incubator has become too cold;

   (d) a stereo hi-fi system;

   (e) as a 'power-on' indicator for a CD player;

   (f) to switch on a high current electric motor by using a small current;

   (g) to indicate which of eight channels a television is tuned into.

7. What does **LED** stand for?

8. (a) Draw the symbol for an LED.

   (b) Indicate which way the electrons flow to make the LED emit light.

9. An LED is connected in a circuit and it emits light. The connections to the LED are then reversed.
   What happens?

10. Why is a resistor needed in series with an LED?

11. *Draw a circuit diagram which will allow an LED to light.*
    Include the series resistor and make sure the LED is connected the correct way to the supply.

12. *An LED is used in a circuit with a 12 V supply.*
    The voltage across the LED is 2 V and the current through it is 10 mA.
    Calculate the value of series resistor that is needed.

13. Describe what a **7-segment display** is.

14. How can different numbers be produced on a 7-segment display?

15. *What is a **binary number**?*

16. *Copy and complete the following table giving the decimal number equivalent for each of the binary numbers in the table.*

BINARY NUMBER	DECIMAL NUMBER
0000	
0001	
0010	
0011	
0100	
0101	
0110	
0111	
1000	
1001	

Section 3 - Input Devices

1. What is meant by an **input device** in an electronic system?

2. Describe the energy change that takes place in a **microphone**.

3. Is a microphone normally used as an analogue or a digital input device?

4. Describe the energy change that takes place in a **thermocouple**.

5. Is a thermocouple an analogue or a digital input device?

6. Describe the energy change that takes place in a **solar cell**.

7. Give <u>two</u> uses for solar cells.

8. What is a **thermistor**?

9. Draw the symbol for a thermistor.

10. Give <u>one</u> use for a thermistor.

11. What is an **LDR**?

12. Draw the symbol for an LDR.

13. Give <u>two</u> uses for an LDR.

14. A thermistor has a resistance of 30 Ω when hot.
    The voltage across it is 9 V.
    Calculate the current in it.

15. An LDR has a current of 10 mA in it and a voltage of 4 V across it.
    Calculate its resistance.

16. What does a **capacitor** do in an electronic circuit?

17. Draw the symbol for a capacitor.

18. What happens to the voltage across a capacitor during the time it is charging?

19. Draw a circuit which could be used to charge a capacitor.

20. Sketch a graph of the voltage across a capacitor during the time it is charging.

21. When does the voltage across a capacitor stop changing?

22. *What does the time taken to charge a capacitor depend on?*

23. *A capacitor is to be charged until the voltage across it reaches the supply voltage.*
    How could the time taken to fully charge <u>*this capacitor*</u> *be reduced, using the same supply voltage?*

24. *How can a charged capacitor be quickly discharged?*

25. *Draw a circuit which can be used as a **voltage divider**.*

26. *(a) State the relationship between V_1, V_2, R_1 and R_2 in the circuit shown.*

    (b) Also state the relationship between V_S, V_1 and V_2, and so give the relationship for V_1 in terms of V_S, R_1 and R_2.

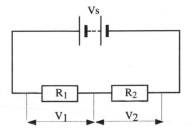

27. *A voltage divider consists of a resistor R_1 of value 1000 Ω in series with a resistor R_2 of value 1500 Ω. It is connected across a supply voltage of 2.5 V.*
    Draw the circuit diagram and calculate the voltage across R_1.

28. *A voltage divider consisting of two resistors is used to 'tap off' exactly half of a supply voltage.*
    What is the relationship between the resistor values?

29. Choose a suitable input device from the following list for each of the applications given.

    microphone; thermocouple; solar cell; thermistor; LDR; capacitor.

    (a) energy source for a satellite;

    (b) time delay before arming a burglar alarm to allow the householder out of the front door;

    (c) temperature control for an aquarium;

    (d) alarm to warn parents in another room when a baby wakes up and cries;

    (e) to measure the temperature inside a furnace;

    (f) circuit to turn down the brightness of a television when the room lights are put out.

30. *Choose a suitable input device for each of the applications given:*

    (a) a coin detector in a drinks machine;

    (b) a fog detector;

    (c) a heartbeat monitor;

    (d) a circuit to switch a hand drier on for 10 s;

    (e) a flame sensor for a gas fire.

Section 4 - Digital Processes

1. Draw the symbol for a **transistor**, labelling the terminals.

2. Give <u>one</u> use for a transistor.

3. A transistor has two possible states - it can be ON or OFF.
   Explain what is meant by this statement.

4. (a) For each of the following circuits state what the circuit does.

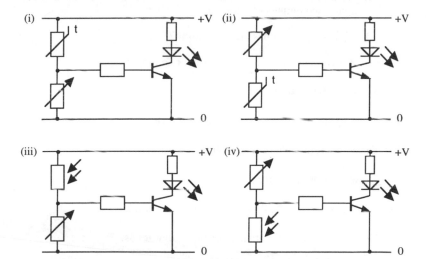

(b) *Explain how each of the above circuits operates.*

5. *What is the purpose of the variable resistor in each of the circuits above?*

6. *A circuit similar to the one shown below can be used as an egg timer,
   lighting an LED after a set time period.*
   *Explain how it works, in particular mentioning the function of
   components **S**, **R**, **C** and the transistor.*

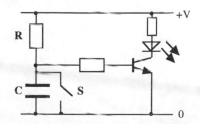

7. What is meant by an electronic **logic gate**?

8. Draw the symbol for a 2-input AND gate.

9. Draw the symbol for a 2-input OR gate.

10. Draw the symbol for a NOT gate.

11. (a) How many different states can the inputs and outputs of logic gates have?

    (b) What <u>three</u> ways can be used to describe the possible states of the inputs and outputs of logic gates?

12. (a) Which logic gate has only one input?

    (b) Which logic gates have more than one input?

13. What is a **truth table**?

14. Draw the truth table for a 2-input AND gate.

15. Draw the truth table for a 2-input OR gate.

16. Draw the truth table for a NOT gate.

17. Explain why the AND gate has the name that it has.

18. Explain why the OR gate has the name that it has.

19. The NOT gate has another name.

    (a) Give this name.

    (b) Explain how the operation of this gate gives rise to this alternative name.

20. *Identify which gates have the following truth tables.*

(a)

INPUT A	B	OUTPUT
0	0	0
0	1	0
1	0	0
1	1	1

(b)

INPUT	OUTPUT
0	1
1	0

(c)

INPUT A	B	OUTPUT
0	0	0
0	1	1
1	0	1
1	1	1

21. (a) Draw an electronic logic circuit which will allow a motor to be switched on by means of one of two switches but <u>only</u> when a master switch has been switched on.

(b) *Complete a truth table for this circuit.*

22. A digital circuit produces an output which is shown below.

What is the name given to this type of circuit?

23. *(a) Draw a circuit for a simple **oscillator** (**clock pulse generator**) using a resistor, a capacitor and a NOT gate (inverter).*

(b) Explain how this circuit operates.

24. *Describe how to change the frequency of the clock pulses generated by a simple oscillator.*

25. There are circuits which can count digital pulses.
    In what form is the output of these counter circuits?

26. The output of a counter circuit can be fed to a **7-segment display** via a **decoder** circuit.

    (a) In what form is the number seen on the 7-segment display?

    (b) What is the function of the decoder circuit?

27. Give <u>two</u> examples of devices containing counter circuits.

Section 5 - Analogue Processes

1. What does an **amplifier** do in an electronic system?

2. State whether or not each of the following electronic systems contains an amplifier:
   radio; intercom; sewing machine; calculator; hi-fi system; model car circuit; CD player; baby alarm.

3. How does the frequency of the output signal from an audio amplifier compare with that of the input signal to the amplifier?

4. How does the amplitude of the output signal from an audio amplifier compare with that of the input signal to the amplifier?

5. Describe what is meant by the **voltage gain** of an amplifier.

6. Give an equation that can be used to calculate the voltage gain of an amplifier.

7. Calculate the voltage gain of an amplifier which has an input voltage of 2 mV and an output voltage of 0.4 V.

8. *Describe how to measure the voltage gain of an amplifier using an oscilloscope.*

9. *Give an equation that links the power P, voltage V and the resistance or impedance R of a circuit.*

10. *Describe what is meant by the **power gain** of an amplifier.*

11. *Give an equation that can be used to calculate the power gain of an amplifier.*

12. *The output power of an amplifier is 20 W. Its input voltage is 10 mV and its input resistance is 10 kΩ.*

    (a) Calculate the input power of the amplifier.

    (b) Calculate the power gain of the amplifier.

UNIT 5 - TRANSPORT

Section 1 - On the Move

1. What is meant by **average speed**?

2. State the relationship between distance, time and average speed.

3. (a) What is the symbol that is used for average speed?

   (b) What is the unit, and its abbreviation, that is used to measure average speed?

4. Describe how to measure the average speed of a runner in a race.
   Your description should include:
   the measurements that have to be made;
   any special points about these measurements;
   how these measurements are made;
   the equation that is used to calculate the speed.

5. A runner completes a 200 m race in 25 s.
   Calculate his average speed.

6. A motorist travels the 72 km from Edinburgh to Glasgow in a time of $1\frac{1}{4}$ hours.
   Calculate the average speed for this journey in metres per second.

7. Calculate how far a supersonic aircraft would travel in one minute while flying at the speed of sound (MACH 1 or 340 m/s).

8. What is meant by **instantaneous speed**?

9. Describe how to measure the instantaneous speed of an object.
   Your description should include:
   the measurements that have to be made;
   any special points about these measurements;
   how these measurements are made;
   the equation that is used to calculate the speed.

10. Two towns are 20 miles apart. The bus journey from one town to the other takes half an hour.

    (a) Calculate the average speed, in miles per hour, for the bus during this journey.

    (b) *At various times during the journey, the bus stops to pick up passengers, travels in heavy traffic in a town centre and travels on a motorway.*
    Explain why the instantaneous speed of the bus varies between 0 and 50 mph.

    (c) *Why are the average and instantaneous speeds of the bus different?*

11. *What is meant by* **reaction time**?

12. *Explain why more accurate results of instantaneous speed are obtained when the timing is carried out using a light gate and an electronic timer rather than by using a manual stopwatch.*

13. Explain what is meant by **speed**.

14. Explain what is meant by **acceleration**.

15. (a) What is the symbol that is used for acceleration?

    (b) What is the unit, and its abbreviation, that is used to measure acceleration?

16. A car advertisement makes the following statement relating to the performance of the car: "0 to 60 mph in 8.2 s."
    What quantity do these figures for the car refer to?

17. Give the equation which links acceleration, change in speed and the time for the change to happen, defining all of the symbols used in the equation.

18. Calculate the acceleration of a car that increases its speed by 10 m/s in 5 s.

19. A car can accelerate from 0 to 60 mph in 8 s.
    Calculate its maximum acceleration in miles per hour per second.

20. Draw the speed time graph for the motion of a car which is travelling at a steady speed of 15 m/s.

21. A car pulls away from rest at traffic lights and reaches a speed of 10 m/s in 8 s.
    Draw the speed-time graph for this motion.

22. The driver of a car sees the traffic lights in the distance change to red and brakes uniformly. The speed of the car reduces from 20 m/s to 5 m/s in 6 s.
    Draw the speed-time graph for this motion.

23. (a) Describe the motion represented by each of the following speed-time graphs.

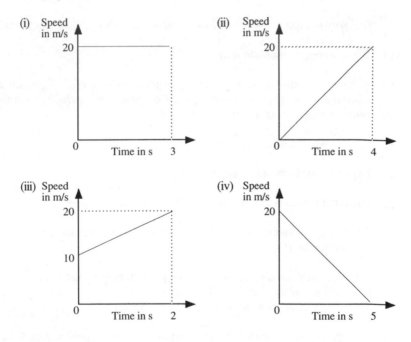

    (b) Calculate the acceleration shown in each of the above speed-time graphs.

24. What is the acceleration of a car which is travelling at a steady speed along a straight level road?

25. (a) What does a negative sign associated with an acceleration value signify?

    (b) What is another term used for a negative acceleration?

26. *How can* **distance travelled** *be calculated from a speed-time graph?*

27. *Consider the following speed-time graph for the motion of a car.*

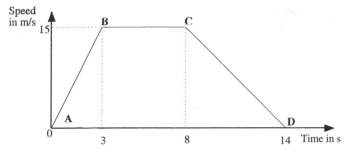

    (a) Describe the motion represented by each section of this graph.

    (b) What is the maximum speed reached by the car?

    (c) Calculate the acceleration shown on the graph.

    (d) Calculate the deceleration shown on the graph.

    (e) Calculate the total distance travelled by the car.

28. *Starting with the definition of acceleration, show that $v = u + at$, where all of the symbols have the usual meanings.*

29. *Calculate the final speed of a train which accelerates uniformly at a rate of 0.6 m/s^2 from a speed of 2 m/s for 30 s.*

30. *A vehicle accelerates from rest to a speed of 6 m/s in 3 s. Calculate its acceleration.*

31. *A ship has a maximum acceleration of 0.1 m/s^2. Calculate the minimum time it would take to increase its speed from 1 m/s to 5 m/s.*

32. *A car, decelerating uniformly at 2 m/s^2, comes to rest in 10 s. Calculate its initial speed.*

Section 2 - Forces at Work

1. Describe <u>three</u> effects that **a force** can have on an object.

2. (a) What is the symbol that is used for force?

   (b) What is the unit, and its abbreviation, that is used to measure force?

3. What is a **newton balance**?
   A diagram will help your description.

4. Describe <u>one</u> use for a newton balance.

5. Copy and complete:

   Weight is a _____ and so it is measured in _____ .

6. State what causes an object to have a weight.

7. *What is meant by the **mass** of an object?*

8. (a) What is the symbol that is used for mass?

   (b) What is the unit, and its abbreviation, that is used to measure mass?

9. *Explain clearly the difference between mass and weight.*
   In your explanation, say which of these quantities is constant for any
   object and which can vary, and explain why this is so.

10. *What is meant by **gravitational field strength**?*

11. *(a) What is the symbol that is used for gravitational field strength?*

    (b) What is the unit, and its abbreviation, that is used to measure
    gravitational field strength?

12. What is the approximate answer when the weight of an object near the
    Earth's surface is divided by its mass?

13. Calculate the weight on Earth of a person who has a mass of 50 kg.

14. Calculate the weight of a 1 kg bag of sugar.

15. A lorry is weighed on a public weigh bridge and is found to have a weight
    of 100 000 N.
    Calculate the mass of the lorry.

16. Explain what is meant by **friction**.

17. (a) Describe three situations where the force of friction is useful.

    (b) Explain how the force of friction can be increased in each of these situations.

18. (a) Describe three situations where the force of friction is unwanted.

    (b) Explain how the force of friction can be decreased in each of these situations.

19. Describe what is meant by **balanced forces** acting on an object.
    Use a diagram to help your description.

20. Describe a situation where two or more forces can act on an object and yet have the same effect as no force at all.
    Include a diagram in your answer.

21. What happens to the speed of an object when it has no forces acting on it?

22. What happens to the speed of an object when it has balanced forces acting on it?

23. A book is sitting on a table.
    What can be said about the forces that are acting on the book?

24. A car is travelling along a straight level road at a constant speed.

    (a) What can be said about the forces acting on the car?

    (b) Explain why the car engine needs to be on to maintain the steady speed

25. Explain why you continually have to pedal a bicycle to move along a straight level road at a constant speed.

26. (a) What is the purpose of seat belts in a car?

    (b) Explain how seat belts in a car do the job that they are designed to do.
    Your explanation should concentrate on the forces involved.

27. *State Newton's First Law of Motion*

28. *Use Newton's First Law of Motion to explain the following situations:*

    (a) why a book sitting on a table does not move;

    (b) how a car can travel along a straight level road at a constant speed;

    (c) why a spaceship in outer space continues moving at the same speed in the same direction.

29. What does an **unbalanced** or **resultant force** cause in an object?

30. What happens to an object when its mass decreases if the unbalanced force acting on it remains the same?

31. What happens to an object when the unbalanced force acting on it increases?

32. A boy on a skateboard is travelling at a constant speed along a straight, level track. His friend jumps on to his skateboard.
    What happens to the motion of the skateboard?

33. A car is travelling at a constant speed along a straight, level road.

    (a) What will happen to the motion of the car if the driver supplies an unbalanced force to it?

    (b) What is the name of the pedal in a car that is used to increase the unbalanced force on the car?

34. *A hot air balloon is falling at a steady speed in the air.*
    What will happen to the balloon if the balloonist throws a sandbag overboard?

35. (a) State the relationship between acceleration, mass and unbalanced or resultant force, using the symbols that are used for these quantities.

    (b) What is the unit, and its abbreviation, that is used for each quantity?

36. A trolley of mass 0.75 kg is acted upon by an unbalanced force of 3 N. Calculate its acceleration.

37. Calculate the unbalanced force that will produce an acceleration of 5 m/s^2 in a mass of 2 kg.

38. An unbalanced force of 1500 N causes a car to decelerate at 2 m/s^2. Calculate the mass of the car.

39. *A car of mass 1000 kg is being driven along a straight, level road. The engine supplies a driving force of 2500 N and the total resistive forces due to friction and air resistance amount to 1000 N.*

    (a) Draw a diagram showing the forces acting on the car.

    (b) Calculate its acceleration.

40. *A parachutist and his parachute have a total mass of 100 kg.*

    (a) Calculate their combined weight.

    (b) The parachutist has a downward acceleration of 0.1 m/s^2. Calculate the unbalanced force acting.

    (c) Calculate the value of the force of air resistance acting on the parachute, and draw a diagram showing all the forces acting.

Section 3 - Movement Means Energy

1. Name the types of energy involved in each of the following situations:

   (a) the energy associated with the fuel used by a vehicle;

   (b) the energy a vehicle has because of its movement;

   (c) the energy a vehicle gains when it goes up a hill;

   (d) the energy that is produced whenever the force of friction is present.

2. (a) What is the symbol that is used for all types of **energy**?

   (b) What is the unit, and its abbreviation, that is used to measure energy?

3. Describe what is meant by an **energy transformation**.

4. Describe the main energy transformations in each of the following situations:

   (a) a vehicle accelerating;

   (b) a vehicle travelling at a constant speed along a straight, level road;

   (c) a vehicle braking to a halt;

   (d) a vehicle going uphill at a constant speed;

   (e) a vehicle going downhill at a constant speed.

5. Copy and complete:

   When work is done by a force, _____ is transferred and the amount of work that is done is a measure of the _____ _____ .

6. (a) There are two symbols that are often used to denote **work done**. State <u>one</u> of them.

   (b) What is the unit, and its abbreviation, that is used to measure work done?

7. (a) State the relationship between work done, force and distance, using the symbols that are used for these quantities.

   (b) What is the unit, and its abbreviation, that is used to measure each quantity?

8. A force of 5 N is used to move a box a distance of 3 m along a bench. Calculate the amount of work done by the force.

9. Calculate the force that is needed to transfer 1000 J of energy a distance of 20 m.

10. 200 J of work are used up by a force of 40 N on an object.
    Calculate the distance that the force moves the object in the direction of the force.

11. (a) What is the symbol that is used for **power**?

    (b) What is the unit, and its abbreviation, that is used to measure power?

12. (a) State the relationship between power, work done and time, using the symbols that are used for these quantities.

    (b) What is the unit, and its abbreviation, that is used to measure each quantity?

13. A force transfers 360 J in 1 minute.
    Calculate the power involved.

14. (a) Show how the relationship between force, distance, time and power can be obtained.

    (b) Show how this expression can be used to obtain a relationship between force, speed and power.

15. What type of energy is gained by an object when work is done to lift it up?

16. Copy and complete:

    The **work done against gravity** is equal to the increase in _____
    _____ _____ of an object.

17. Under what circumstances is work done on an object by gravity?

18. (a) What is the symbol that is used for **gravitational potential energy**?

    (b) What is the unit, and its abbreviation, that is used to measure gravitational potential energy?

19. (a) State the relationship which is used to calculate gravitational potential energy, using the symbols that are used for each quantity.

    (b) What is the unit, and its abbreviation, that is used to measure each quantity?

20. A 50 kg bag of cement is raised 1.5 m on to the back of a lorry. Calculate the gravitational potential energy gained by the bag of cement.

21. A person of mass 60 kg runs up a flight of stairs in 10 s. The vertical height of the stairs is 5 m.

    (a) Calculate the weight of the person.

    (b) Calculate the amount of work done.

    (c) Calculate the power developed by the person in running up the stairs.

22. A small electric motor lifts a mass of 0.3 kg at a speed of 20 cm/s. Calculate the power developed by the motor.

23. What type of energy does an object have because of its motion?

24. Copy and complete:

    The greater the _____ and/or the greater the _____ of a moving object, the greater is its kinetic energy.

25. *(a) What is the symbol that is used for* **kinetic energy**?

    (b) What is the unit, and its abbreviation, that is used to measure kinetic energy?

26. *(a) State the relationship between kinetic energy, mass and speed.*

    (b) What is the unit, and its abbreviation, that is used to measure each quantity?

27. Calculate the amount of kinetic energy a trolley of mass 0.75 kg has when it is travelling at 2 m/s.

28. Show by calculation, which has the greater amount of kinetic energy, a car of mass 800 kg travelling at 26 m/s (about 60 mph) or a lorry of mass 3 tonnes travelling at 13 m/s (about 30 mph).
    (One tonne = 1000 kg)

29. State and explain the **principle of conservation of energy**.

30. A crane lifts a crate of mass 60 kg through a height of 25 m in a time of one minute.

    (a) Calculate the gravitational potential energy gained by the crate.

    (b) Ignoring the mass of the crane jib, calculate the output power of the crane.

    (c) If the cable of the crane breaks when it has completed the lifting operation, calculate the maximum velocity of the crate just as it reaches the ground (ignoring air resistance).

31. Show that, if air resistance can be ignored, the speed of a falling object is independent of its mass and depends only on the height through which it moves.

32. A stone falls from a cliff which is 80 m high.

    (a) If air resistance can be ignored, calculate the speed at which it enters the water at the bottom of the cliff.

    (b) If air resistance cannot be ignored, what effect will this have on the speed of the stone as it enters the water?

    (c) In practice, not all of the initial gravitational potential energy is transferred into kinetic energy.
    Other than kinetic energy, what is the main form of energy produced?

UNIT 6 - ENERGY MATTERS

Section 1 - Supply and Demand

1. Explain what a **fossil fuel** is.

2. Give <u>three</u> examples of fossil fuels.

3. Which types of fuels are at present our main sources of energy?

4. "The reserves of fossil fuels are finite."
   Explain what is meant by this statement.

5. What is meant by **conserving** energy?

6. Explain why it is important to conserve energy.

7. State <u>three</u> ways of conserving energy in industry.

8. State <u>three</u> ways of conserving energy in the home.

9. State <u>three</u> ways of conserving energy in transport.

10. (a) Calculate the number of kilowatt-hours of energy that are wasted if 1000 people each leave one 100 W light bulb on unnecessarily for one hour.

    (b) Calculate the cost of this wasted energy if each kilowatt-hour costs 10 p.

11. Explain what is meant by a **renewable** source of energy.

12. Explain what is meant by a **non-renewable** source of energy.

13. (a) List at least <u>three</u> renewable sources of energy.

(b) For each of the sources of energy in your list, state how it can be harnessed or made use of.

(c) *Explain the <u>advantages</u> associated with each of the sources of energy in your list.*

(d) *Explain the <u>disadvantages</u> associated with each of the sources of energy in your list.*

14. List at least <u>three</u> non-renewable sources of energy.

Section 2 - Generation of Electricity

1. What is a **power station**?

2. Some power stations are known as **thermal** power stations.
   Why thermal?

3. (a) List the main stages of a thermal power station on the block diagram.

   (b) State the main energy transformation that takes place at each stage.

4. (a) List the main stages of a hydro-electric power station on the block diagram.

   (b) State the main energy transformation that takes place at each stage.

5. Four tonnes of water every second are allowed to fall through a height of 50 m from behind a dam in a hydro-electric power scheme.
   Calculate the power available from this water. (1 tonne = 1000 kg)

6. (a) Describe the principle of a **pumped storage hydro-electric scheme**.

   (b) State the advantages of a pumped storage hydro-electric scheme.

7. (a) List the main stages of a nuclear power station on the block diagram.

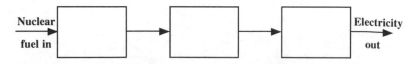

   (b) State the main energy transformation that takes place at each stage.

8. What is the most common fuel that is used in a nuclear power station?

9. *Explain how the fuel is used in a nuclear power station to produce a controlled amount of heat.*
   Your explanation should include the following terms:
       neutron;
       uranium nucleus;
       heat;
       moderator;
       chain reaction.

10. *Each gram of uranium used in a nuclear power station can give 8.2×10^{10} J of energy. Each tonne of coal used in a thermal power station can give 2.8×10^{10} J of energy.*
    Compare the amount of energy available from equal masses of coal and nuclear fuel.
    (1 tonne = 1000 kg)

11. State one of the major disadvantages of nuclear reactors.

12. *Give the equation that is used to calculate the **efficiency** of an energy transformation.*

13. *A thermal power station uses 50 tonnes of coal every hour. Each tonne of coal can give 2.8×10^{10} J of energy.*

    (a) Calculate the input energy every second.

    (b) If the power station is 15 % efficient, calculate its power output.

14. *Explain what is meant by the statement that 'energy is **degraded** in an energy transformation'.*

Section 3 - Source to Consumer

1. Replace the word 'induced' with another suitable word in the following statement.
   "A voltage was induced in a conductor".

2. Under what circumstances will a voltage be **induced** in a conductor?

3. Draw <u>two</u> diagrams to illustrate two <u>different</u> situations where a voltage is induced in a conductor.

4. *There are <u>three</u> factors that affect the size of the voltage induced in a conductor.*

   (a) What are these factors?

   (b) How does each of them affect the size of the induced voltage?

5. There are <u>two</u> other names that are sometimes used for an **a.c. generator**. What are these other names?

6. (a) Label the main parts of an a.c. generator on the diagram, using each of the following terms:
   input; rotor; stator coil; iron core; output.

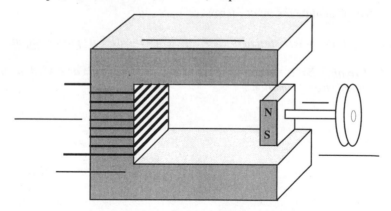

   (b) Use the labelled diagram to explain how an a.c. generator works.

   (c) Where are a.c. generators such as the one shown in the diagram often used?

7. *There are several differences between full-sized a.c. generators and the simple working model generator studied in class.*

   (a) List these differences.

   (b) Explain the reasons for the differences.

8. State what **transformers** are used for.

9. Describe the construction of a transformer.
   Use a labelled diagram to help your description.

10. *Explain how transformers can be used to change the size of an a.c. voltage. Make sure your explanation includes why transformers only work with a.c. voltages.*

11. Give the relationship between V_s, V_p, n_s and n_p for a transformer and say what each of these terms means.

12. (a) What is meant by a 'step-up' transformer?

    (b) What is meant by a 'step-down' transformer?

13. A mains transformer used for a model train set has an output voltage of 12 V.
    Calculate the number of turns on the secondary winding if there are 2300 turns on the primary.

14. A transformer has an input voltage of 11 000 V. There are 55 000 turns on its primary winding and 1150 turns on its secondary winding.

    (a) Is the transformer a step-up or a step-down transformer?

    (b) Calculate the output voltage of the transformer.

15. *Explain why transformers are not 100 % efficient. You should be able to give at least <u>three</u> reasons why transformers are not 100 % efficient.*

16. *(a) Give an equation that can be used to calculate the **input power** to a transformer, defining each of the terms used in the equation.*

    *(b) Give an equation that can be used to calculate the **output power** from a transformer, defining each of the terms used in the equation.*

17. *Give an equation that can be used to calculate the **efficiency** of a transformer.*

18. *A mains transformer, with 1840 turns on its primary winding and 40 turns on its secondary winding, is used in a battery charger.*

    *(a) Calculate the **turns ratio** of the transformer.*

    (b) Calculate the output voltage.

    (c) If the primary current is 0.1 A and the secondary current is 3.5 A, calculate the efficiency of the transformer.

19. When electricity is transmitted long distances, power is lost.

    (a) Why is power lost?

    (b) State the equation that is used to calculate the power loss during transmission, defining all of the terms used in the equation.

    (c) State and explain how the power loss is kept as low as possible.

20. Draw a diagram of a model **power transmission system**.
    Include the following on your diagram:
    'power station' end;
    step-up transformer;
    high voltage transmission lines;
    step-down transformer;
    'village' end.

21. *Electricity is transmitted along transmission lines which have a resistance of 0.2 ohms per kilometre (Ω/km). The two transmission lines are each 25 km long.*
    If the electricity is transmitted at a current of 20 A, calculate the total power lost in the transmission lines.

22. Describe how electrical energy is transmitted by the **National Grid** system.

Section 4 - Heat in the Home

1. Copy and complete:

   (a) _____ is a measure of how hot or cold an object is. It is measured
   in _____ _____ .

   (b) Heat is a form of _____ and is measured in _____ .

   (c) Putting _____ into an object usually makes its _____ increase.

2. Copy and complete the following sentence using the words below.
   higher; lower

   Heat travels from a region of _____ temperature to a region of
   _____ temperature.

3. (a) Name the three ways that heat can travel.

   (b) Describe how heat travels in each of these three ways, indicating for
   each the types of materials that allow heat to be transfered and the
   part played by the particles of the material.

4. Describe, mentioning the method of heat loss that is principally reduced,
   how each of the following reduces heat loss in the home.

   (a) double glazing;

   (b) cavity wall insulation;

   (c) loft insulation;

   (d) insulating the hot water cylinder with a blanket,

   (e) using metal foil on walls behind radiators.

5. What does heat loss in a given time depend upon?

6. Does 1 kg of copper need the same amount of energy as 1 kg of
   aluminium to raise its temperature by 1 °C?

7. Compare the amount of energy needed to raise the temperature of 2 kg of copper by 1 ºC with that needed to do the same to 1 kg of copper.

8. Compare the amount of energy needed to raise the temperature of 1 kg of copper by 1 ºC with that needed to raise the temperature by 2 ºC.

9. Compare the amount of energy needed to raise the temperature of 1 kg of copper from 9 ºC to 10 ºC with that needed to raise the temperature from 99 ºC to 100 ºC.

10. Explain what is meant by the **specific heat capacity** of a substance.

11. (a) What is the symbol that is used for specific heat capacity?

    (b) What is the unit, and its abbreviation, that is used to measure specific heat capacity?

12. (a) State the equation that links heat to the mass, specific heat capacity and temperature change in a substance.

    (b) What is the unit, and its abbreviation, that is used to measure each quantity?

13. Calculate the amount of heat needed to increase the temperature of 1 kg of aluminium by 10 ºC.
    (The specific heat capacity of aluminium is 902 J/kg ºC.)

14. Calculate the amount of heat needed to raise the temperature of 2 kg of water from 20 ºC to 90 ºC.
    (The specific heat capacity of water is 4180 J/kg ºC.)

15. Calculate the increase in temperature of the 5 kg of coolant in the cooling system of a car after it has absorbed 720 kJ of energy from the car engine.
    (The specific heat capacity of the coolant used is 2400 J/kg ºC.)

16. *An electric kettle is rated at 2.2 kW and has a capacity of 1.5 litres of water.*
    Calculate how long it would take to increase the temperature of the water from room temperature (20 ºC) to boiling point, without boiling any water off.
    (The specific heat capacity of water is 4180 J/kg ºC;
    mass of 1 litre of water is 1 kg.)

17. *A car of mass 1000 kg, travelling at 4 m/s, is brought to rest by applying the brakes.*
    Calculate the increase in temperature of the brake linings and pads if all of the original kinetic energy of the car is transferred to heat in the brakes.
    (Total mass of brake lining material = 0.5 kg;
    specific heat capacity of brake lining material – 500 J/kg °C.)

18. What are the <u>three</u> **states of matter**?

19. (a) What <u>two</u> things <u>can</u> happen to an object when heat is transferred to it?

    (b) Explain how to decide which of the two things <u>will</u> happen in any particular case.

20. Copy and complete the diagram, giving the names of the processes missing from the boxes.

21. What does <u>not</u> change when the state of a substance is changed?

22. (a) What must be added to a substance to make its state change from a solid to a liquid or from a liquid to a gas?

    (b) What is lost from a substance when its state changes from a gas to a liquid or from a liquid to a solid?

23. Give <u>two</u> examples of applications which involve a change of state and for each of them explain how they work.

24. *(A bit of an aside, but still relevant!)*
    A refrigerator is left working with its door open in a perfectly heat-sealed room, that is a room where no heat can enter or leave (if such a room were to exist).
    What will happen to the temperature in the room?
    Will it increase, decrease or stay the same?

25. (a) What does the word 'latent' mean?

    (b) Hence explain how the term 'latent heat' comes about.

26. (a) Give another word which means the same as 'fusion'.

    (b) Give another term which is often used for 'vaporisation'.

27. (a) Explain what is meant by the **latent heat of fusion** of a substance.

    (b) Explain what is meant by the **latent heat of vaporisation** of a substance.

28. *(a) What is the symbol that is used for **specific latent heat**?*

    (b) What is the unit, and its abbreviation, that is used to measure specific latent heat?

29. *(a) State the equation that links heat to the mass and the specific latent heat of a substance.*

    (b) What is the unit, and its abbreviation, that is used to measure each quantity?

30. *Calculate the amount of heat needed to convert 0.5 kg of water at its boiling point into steam.*
    (The specific latent heat of vaporisation of water is 2.26 x 10⁶ J/kg.)

31. *Calculate the amount of heat given out when 0.5 kg of water freezes to ice at 0 ⁰C.*
    (The specific latent heat of fusion of water is 3.34 x 10⁵ J/kg.)

32. *A lump of ice of mass 1 kg is removed from a freezer at a temperature of –18 ⁰C.*
    Calculate the amount of heat which it must be given in order to completely convert it to steam at 100 ⁰C.
    (Note that although this problem may be considered difficult, it will be found to be easier if treated logically.)
    (The specific heat capacity of ice is 2100 J/kg ⁰C;
    the specific heat capacity of water is 4180 J/kg ⁰C;
    the specific latent heat of fusion of water is 3.34 x 10⁵ J/kg;
    the specific latent heat of vaporisation of water is 2.26 x 10⁶ J/kg.)

Unit 7 - Space physics

Section 1 - Signals from Space

1. Copy and complete the following sentences using words chosen from the list below.
   (You will have to use some words more than once and sometimes use the plural of the word.)
   galaxy; moon; planet; solar system; star; sun; universe.

   (a) The _____ consists of a large number of _____, such as the Milky Way and Andromeda, each separated by empty space.

   (b) Each _____ consists of millions of _____, of which Proxima Centauri is the second closest to the Earth, the closest to the Earth being _____.

   (c) The Earth is one of nine _____, each of which orbits around the _____. Such a group of heavenly bodies is known as a _____.

   (d) Like the Earth, some of the _____ in our own and in other _____ have natural satellites which orbit around them. These satellites are called _____.

2. Copy and complete:

   (a) The collection of all known galaxies is called the _____.

   (b) A _____ consists of a large number of stars and solar systems.

   (c) A heavenly body which emits light and heat energy is called a _____.

   (d) The nearest star to the Earth is _____.

   (e) Some stars, like the Sun, have several _____ orbiting round them.

   (f) A star, together with the heavenly bodies associated with it, is collectively known as a _____.

   (g) Some planets have one or more natural satellites, which are called _____, orbiting round them.

3. State the approximate time it takes light to travel to Earth from each of the following places in the universe:

   (a) the Sun;

   (b) the next nearest star, Proxima Centauri;

   (c) the furthest edge of our galaxy.

4. At what speed does light travel?

5. *(a) What is a **light year** a unit of?*

   (b) Calculate the size of one light year.

   (c) Explain why it is necessary to use a light year as a unit in astronomy.

6. An astronomical telescope is sometimes called a **refracting telescope**. Explain where this name comes from.

7. Draw a diagram showing and naming the <u>three</u> main parts of a refracting telescope.

8. (a) Name the <u>two</u> lenses used in a refracting telescope.

   (b) State the job done by each of them.

9. *Explain what happens to the image when the diameter of the objective lens in a refracting telescope is increased.*

10. *Explain what a **magnifying glass** is.*

11. *(a) When drawing ray diagrams, what <u>two</u> rays coming from the object are important?*

    (b) Why are they important in locating the image that the lens forms of the object?

12. *Draw a ray diagram to show how an image is formed by a magnifying glass.*

13. *Describe the image formed by a magnifying glass.*

14. (a) Draw a labelled diagram showing what a prism does to a beam of white light.

    (b) Why does a prism have this effect on a beam of white light?

15. State the colours of the **visible spectrum** in order.

16. List the following colours in order of **decreasing** wavelength:
    blue;
    green;
    red.

17. Explain what is meant by a **line spectrum**.

18. Why are line spectra useful?

19. *(a) Name the <u>seven</u> types of radiation which collectively are known as the **electromagnetic spectrum**.*

    (b) What do all of these radiations have in common?

    (c) What properties are different for the radiations in this family of waves?

20. *(a) Copy and complete the following table to include all seven types of radiation in the electromagnetic spectrum.*

    (b) Name a detector for each of the types of radiation.

Type of radiation	Wavelength	Frequency	Detector
	SHORTEST ▲	HIGHEST ▲	
	▼	▼	
	LONGEST	LOWEST	

21. What type of waves, other than light waves, can be detected by special kinds of telescope?

22. *Explain why different kinds of telescope are needed to detect the signals that come to Earth from space.*

Section 2 - Space Travel

1. What causes a rocket in space to move forward?

2. Explain the following situations using the rule:
   "**A** pushes **B**, **B** pushes **A** back".
   In each case, draw a diagram with forces on it to help your explanation and say which object you mean as **A** and which object you mean as **B**.

   (a) Explain how a car moves forward along a road.

   (b) Explain how a chair can support a person sitting on it.

   (c) Explain how a rocket moves forward in space.

3. *State **Newton's Third Law**.*

4. *What is meant by **"Newton Pairs"**?*

5. *Identify the "Newton Pairs" acting on the helicopter shown.*

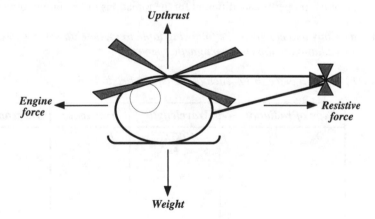

6. *Identify the "Newton Pairs" acting on the boat shown.*

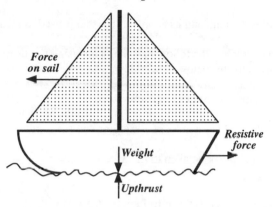

7. *Although they are different, "Newton Pairs" are often confused with balanced forces.*
   Explain clearly the difference between balanced forces and "Newton Pairs".

8. What is meant by **thrust**?

9. A booster rocket motor is fired on a spacecraft which is far away from any planets. The rocket motor supplies a thrust of 2000 N.
   If the mass of the spacecraft is 5000 kg, calculate the acceleration produced.

10. (a) Explain why a rocket motor does not need to be kept on all the time while the rocket is moving far away from any planets.

    (b) What would happen to a rocket in space if the rocket motor was fired?

11. (a) What is the name of the force that acts on an object because of its mass?

    (b) What can be noted about the acceleration of all objects near to the Earth's surface due to this force acting on the objects, if the effects of friction can be ignored?

12. State the approximate value of the acceleration due to gravity near the Earth's surface.

13. (a) What is meant by the **weight** of an object?

    (b) What is the unit, and its abbreviation, that is used to measure weight?

14. Copy and complete the following statements using words or phrases chosen from the list below:

    stays the same; changes; becomes zero.

    A block of metal has a mass of 1 kilogram on the Earth.

    (a) When the block is taken to the Moon, its mass _____ , and its weight _____ .

    (b) When the block is taken to Jupiter, its mass _____ , and its weight _____ .

    (c) When the block is taken into space, far away from any planets, its mass _____ , and its weight _____ .

15. *What is a **gravitational field**?*

16. *(a) What is meant by **gravitational field strength**?*

    (b) What is the unit, and its abbreviation, that is used to measure gravitational field strength?

17. *State the value of the gravitational field strength near the Earth's surface.*

18. *Explain how acceleration due to gravity and the gravitational field strength are both equal.*

19. *It might be possible, although unlikely, for an astronaut of the future to go 'space-hopping' from planet to planet.*
    Calculate the total weight of the spaceman and his spacesuit on each of the planets given in the table, if their combined mass is 120 kg.

Planet	Gravitational field strength (N/kg)
Venus	9
Earth	10
Mars	4
Jupiter	26

20. *A piece of equipment which has a weight of 25 N on Earth is taken to the Moon where the acceleration due to gravity is 1.6 m/s^2.*
    Calculate its weight on the Moon.

21. Under what conditions is an object **weightless**?

22. An object can sometimes appear weightless when it is not actually so. Explain how this can be.

23. *Copy and complete the following statements, using words or phrases chosen from the following list.*
    acceleration due to gravity;
    gravitational field strength;
    inertia;
    mass;
    weight.

    (a) The amount of matter in an object is known as its _____ .

    (b) The force of gravity acting on an object is known as its _____ .

    (c) Any object which has a mass also has a reluctance to have its motion changed.
    This property is known as its _____ .

    (d) The ratio of weight to mass for an object close to the surface of a planet is known as that planet's _____ .

    (e) Although they have different units, two quantities are equivalent to each other.
    These quantities are gravitational field strength and _____ .

24. *What happens to the weight of a body as it gets further away from the surface of the Earth?*

25. If an object is projected horizontally, it does not continue to move horizontally.

    (a) Describe the path it takes.

    (b) Explain what causes it to follow this path.

26. *The path of a projectile can be treated as two independent motions.*

    (a) Describe and explain the horizontal motion of a projectile.

    (b) Describe and explain the vertical motion of a projectile.

27. *There is only one quantity that is common to the vertical and horizontal motions of a projectile.*
    What is it?

28. *A food parcel is dropped from a helicopter which is flying horizontally at a speed of 50 m/s.*
    If the parcel takes 4 s to reach the ground and air resistance can be ignored, calculate:

    (a) the horizontal speed of the parcel just as it reaches the ground;

    (b) the horizontal distance travelled by the parcel;

    (c) the vertical speed of the parcel just as it reaches the ground;

    (d) the height of the helicopter when the parcel was dropped.

29. *By considering the motion of a projectile, explain how a satellite remains in orbit.*

30. (a) What type of energy does a spacecraft have because of its movement?

    (b) What is this energy changed into when the spacecraft re-enters the Earth's atmosphere from space?

    (c) What causes this energy transformation to take place?

31. The orbiter part of the Space Shuttle, the part that returns to Earth after the space mission, has a mass of 70 000 kg. While in orbit, its speed is about 8000 m/s and at touchdown its speed is about 100 m/s.

(a) Calculate the kinetic energy of the orbiter while it is in orbit.

(b) Calculate the kinetic energy of the orbiter just as it touches down.

(c) What has happened to the 'lost' kinetic energy between being in orbit and at touchdown?

(d) The average force needed to stop the orbiter as it travels along the runway between touchdown and coming to rest is 175 kN. Calculate the length of the runway needed.

32. A meteorite consists of a lump of iron of mass 3 kg. It enters the Earth's atmosphere at 2000 m/s.
Assuming 10 % of the kinetic energy of the meteorite is converted into heat (which in fact does not happen), calculate its rise in temperature.
(The specific heat capacity of iron is 440 J/kg ^oC.)

PREFIXES

You should know the following prefixes and their meaning in Scientific Notation:

Tera (T)	-	10^{12}
Giga (G)	-	10^{9}
Mega (M)	-	10^{6}
kilo (k)	-	10^{3}
milli (m)	-	10^{-3}
micro (μ)	-	10^{-6}
nano (n)	-	10^{-9}
pico (p)	-	10^{-12}

PHYSICAL QUANTITIES

The quantities that you should know about for Standard Grade Physics are listed in the table below.
Copy and complete each row in the table as you come across the quantity in your revision.

PHYSICAL QUANTITY	SYMBOL	UNIT and ABBREVIATION	
Basic S.I. Units			
mass	m	kilogram	kg
length (distance)	d	metre	m
time	t	second	s
Other S.I. Units			
acceleration			
acceleration due to gravity			
activity (of a radioactive source)			
average speed			
charge			
current (electric)			
electrical energy			
energy (work done)			
equivalent dose			
force			
frequency			
gravitational field strength			
heat			
kinetic energy			
periodic time			
potential energy			
power (rate of using energy)			
power of a lens			
resistance (electrical)			
specific heat capacity			
specific latent heat			
speed			
temperature			
voltage			
wavelength			
weight (force due to gravity)			
work			

FORMULAE

To make formulae easier to find they have been grouped under three headings:

formulae relating to Energy

because all types of energy are interchangeable,

and

formulae used in Mechanics, Waves and Heat;

formulae used in Electricity.

Formulae in *italics* relate to Credit Level. All others relate to General Level.

Formulae relating to Energy

power $= \dfrac{\text{energy}}{\text{time}}$

$P = \dfrac{E}{t}$

work done (energy used up) $=$ force x distance

$E_w = F\,d$

gravitational potential energy $= m\,g\,h$

$E_p = m\,g\,h$

kinetic energy $= {}^1/_2\,m\,v^2$

$E_k = {}^1/_2\,m\,v^2$

electrical energy $=$ current x time x voltage

$E_e = I\,t\,V$

heat $= c\,m\,\Delta T$ (for a change in temperature)

$E_h = c\,m\,\Delta T$

heat $= m\,l$ (for a change in state)

$E_h = m\,l$

Formulae used in Mechanics, Waves and Heat

speed $\quad=\dfrac{\text{distance}}{\text{time}}$ $\qquad v = \dfrac{d}{t}$

average speed $\quad=\dfrac{\text{total distance travelled}}{\text{total time taken}}$ $\qquad \dot{v} = \dfrac{d}{t}$

speed $\quad=$ frequency x wavelength $\qquad v = f\,\lambda$

wave period $\quad=\dfrac{1}{\textit{frequency}}$ $\qquad T = \dfrac{1}{f}$

acceleration $\quad=\dfrac{\text{change in speed}}{\text{time for change}}$ $\qquad a = \dfrac{\Delta v}{t} = \dfrac{v-u}{t}$

$\qquad\qquad\qquad\qquad\qquad\qquad\qquad v = u + a\,t$

acceleration $\quad=\dfrac{\text{unbalanced force}}{\text{mass}}$ $\qquad a = \dfrac{F}{m}$

work done $\quad=$ force x distance $\qquad E_w = F\,d$

power $\quad=\dfrac{\text{energy}}{\text{time}}$ $\qquad P = \dfrac{E}{t}$

power $\quad=$ force x speed $\qquad P = F\,v$

gravitational $\quad=$ m g h $\qquad E_p = m\,g\,h$
 potential energy

kinetic energy $\quad=\ ^{1}/_{2}\,m\,v^2$ $\qquad E_k = \ ^{1}/_{2}\,m\,v^2$

$v = \sqrt{(2\,g\,h)}\quad$ *(if air resistance can be ignored)*

weight $\quad=$ m g $\qquad W = m\,g$

efficiency $\quad=\dfrac{\textit{useful energy output}}{\textit{total energy input}}$ $\qquad efficiency = \dfrac{E_{out}}{E_{in}}$

power (of a lens) $\quad=\dfrac{1}{\textit{focal length}}$ $\qquad power = \dfrac{1}{f}$

heat $\quad=$ c m ΔT $\qquad E_h = c\,m\,\Delta T$
 (for a change in temperature)

heat $\quad=$ m l *(for a change in state)* $\qquad E_h = m\,l$

Formulae used in Electricity

charge $\quad\quad\quad\quad$ = *current x time* $\quad\quad\quad\quad\quad\quad\quad\quad$ $Q \;\; = \;\; I\,t$

voltage $\quad\quad\quad$ = current x resistance $\quad\quad\quad\quad$ $V \;\; = \;\; I\,R$

power $\quad\quad\quad$ = $\dfrac{\text{energy}}{\text{time}}$ $\quad\quad\quad\quad\quad\quad\quad\quad\quad$ $P \;\; = \;\; \dfrac{E}{t}$

power $\quad\quad\quad$ = current x voltage $\quad\quad$ $P \;\; = \;\; I\,V \;\; = \;\; I^2\,R \;\; = \;\; \dfrac{V^2}{R}$

electrical energy $\;$ = current x time x voltage $\quad\quad\quad$ $E_e \;\; = \;\; I\,t\,V$

$R_T \quad = \quad R_1 + R_2 + R_3 + \;\_\;\_\;\_\;\_\;$ *(for resistors in series)*

$\dfrac{1}{R_T} \quad = \quad \dfrac{1}{R_1} + \dfrac{1}{R_2} + \dfrac{1}{R_3} + \;\_\;\_\;\_\;\_\;$ *(for resistors in parallel)*

$\dfrac{V_1}{V_2} \quad = \quad \dfrac{R_1}{R_2} \quad$ *(for a voltage divider)*

voltage gain $\;\; = \;\; \dfrac{V_{out}}{V_{in}}$

power gain $\;\; = \;\; \dfrac{P_{out}}{P_{in}}$

efficiency $\;\; = \;\; \dfrac{\text{useful energy output}}{\text{total energy input}}$ $\quad\quad$ *efficiency* $\;\; = \;\; \dfrac{E_{out}}{E_{in}}$

$\dfrac{V_s}{V_p} \quad = \quad \dfrac{n_s}{n_p} \quad = \quad \dfrac{I_p}{I_s} \quad$ (for a transformer)

ANSWERS TO NUMERICAL QUESTIONS

UNIT 1 - TELECOMMUNICATION

Section 1 - Communication Using Waves

8. 1700 m (1.7 km)

9. 340 m/s

11. 1020 m

12. 4 s

20. 2.5 m/s

21. 15 m

22. 3 s

24. 4 m/s

25. 1.30 m

26. 0.5 Hz

Section 2 - Communication Using Cables

26. *0.055 s*

Section 4 - Transmission of Radio Waves

5. $3.6 \times 10^8 m$

7. *330 m*

8. *1546 kHz*

Unit 2 - Using electricity

Section 2 - Alternating and Direct Current

16. *3 A*

17. *900 C*

Section 3 - Resistance

12. 4 Ω

13. 0.05 A (50 mA)

14. 10 V

29. 9000 J (9 kJ)

31. 36 W

32. 1 A

34. *0.25 W*

35. *960 Ω*

Section 4 - Useful Circuits

23. *125 Ω*

24. *1.25 Ω*

UNIT 3 - HEALTH PHYSICS

Section 3 - Light and Sight

23. *2.5 D*

24. *10 cm*

Section 5 - Nuclear Radiation - Humans and Medicine

22. *100 kBq*

23. *2 years*

UNIT 4 - ELECTRONICS

Section 2 - Output Devices

12. *1000 Ω*

Section 3 - Input Devices

14. 0.3 A

15. 400 Ω

27. *1.5 V*

Section 5 - Analogue Processes

7. 200

12. *(a) 1 x 10^{-8} W*

    (b) 2 x 10^9

Unit 5 - Transport

Section 1 - On the Move

5. 8 m/s

6. 16 m/s

7. 20 400 m (20.4 km)

10. (a) 40 mph

18. 2 m/s^2

19. 7.5 miles per hour per second

23. (b) (i)   acceleration is zero
    (ii)   5 m/s^2
    (iii) 5 m/s^2
    (iv) -4 m/s^2

27. *(b) 15 m/s*
    (c)   5 m/s^2
    (d) -4 m/s^2
    (e) 142.5 m

29. *20 m/s^2*

30. *2 m/s^2*

31. *40 s*

32. *20 m/s*

Section 2 - Forces at Work

13. 500 N

14. 10 N

15. 10 000 kg

36. 4 m/s^2

37. 10 N

38. 750 kg

39. *1.5 m/s^2*

40. *(a) 1000 N*
    (b) 10 N downwards
    (c) 990 N

Section 3 - Movement Means Energy

8. 15 J

9. 50 N

10. 5 m

13. 6 W

20. 750 J

21. (a) 600 N
    (b) 3000 J
    (c) 300 W

22. 0.6 W

27. *1.5 J*

28. *Car: 270 400 J*
    Lorry: 253 500 J
    *The **car** has the greater amount of kinetic energy.*

30. *(a) 15 000 J*
    (b) 250 W
    (c) 22.36 m/s

32. *(a) 40 m/s*

Unit 6 - Energy matters

Section 1 - Supply and Demand

10. (a) 100 kW h
    (b) £10.00

Section 2 - Generation of Electricity

5. 2 MW

10. *1 gram of uranium gives 2.93 x 10^6 times as much energy as 1 gram of coal.*

13. (a) *3.89 x 10^8 J*
    (b) *58.3 MW*

Section 3 - Source to Consumer

13. 120 turns

14. (b) 230 V

18. (a) *46 (or 46:1)*
    (b) *5 V*
    (c) *76 %*

21. *4 kW*

Section 4 - Heat in the Home

13. 9020 J

14. 585 200 J   (585.2 kJ)

15. 60 °C

16. *228 s (3 min 48 s)*

17. *32 °C*

17. *32 ºC*

30. *1.13 x 10⁶ J*

31. *1.67 x 10⁵ J*

32. *3 049 800 J*

Unit 7 - Space physics

Section 1 - Signals from Space

5. *(b)* 9.46×10^{15} *m*

Section 2 - Space Travel

9. 0.4 m/s^2

19. *Weight on Venus = 1080 N*
    Weight on Earth = 1200 N
    Weight on Mars = 480 N
    Weight on Jupiter = 3120 N

20. *4 N*

28. *(a) 50 m/s*
    (b) 200 m
    (c) 40 m/s
    (d) 80 m

31. *(a) 2.24 $\times$ 10^{12} J*
    (b) 3.5 $\times$ 10^8 J
    (d) 2000 m (2 km)

32. *455 ^{o}C*